FARTS MAKE NOISE

DUKE THE DEAF DOG ASL SERIES

By Kelly Brakenhoff

Illustrated by Theresa Murray

Emerald Prairie
PRESS

This publication was made possible in part by a grant from the West Omaha Sertoma Club.

Copyright 2020 by Emerald Prairie Press

Photographs by Robert Chadwick of Robert Chadwick Photography

Published by Emerald Prairie Press, August 31, 2020

Cover Design and Interior Layout by Melissa Williams Design

Supplemental video content available on www.kellybrakenhoff.com

ISBN 978-1-7337424-3-6 (Print)

To Dave and our children:
Joe, Jon, Kate, James, Claire & Colton.
Before you all came along, I would never have
*considered placing the word **farts** on a book cover.*

—Kelly

To my supportive husband, Shawn, and our boys,
Daniel and Liam.
Thanks for knowing when to say,
"excuse me." If only our dog could be so polite.

—Theresa

Other Books by Kelly Brakenhoff

Cassandra Sato Mysteries
Dead End (Short Story)
Death by Dissertation
Dead Week
Dead of Winter Break

Duke the Deaf Dog ASL Series
Never Mind

In the **morning**,
I ate my cereal.

Mom said, "Scoop your cereal without scraping the bowl. Banging on the dishes is loud."

I helped my mom do chores before **school.**

Mom said, "Be gentle. Dropping forks and spoons is loud."

My teacher was talking during pre-K.
I felt fidgety.

Teacher said,

"Please stop tapping your crayons.

Repeating noises **bother** people."

5

Our school had a **fire drill**.

The alarm beeped, the light flashed, and we moved quickly. Fire alarms are very loud.

When we walked back to the classroom, my teacher said, "Pick up your feet when you walk. Your feet make noise shuffling on the floor."

We walked my brothers home from school.

Bees buzz, but they are quiet.

I asked, "What noise do **butterflies** make?"

Mom said, "Butterflies don't make any noise."

My brother said, "Ohhh, you farted!"
Mom said, "Say 'excuse me'."

I said, "Huh? It didn't **stink**.
How did you know?"

My brother laughed, "Farts make noise, bro!"
I said, "Excuse me." Then I laughed too.

At dinner time, the pizza in the oven **smelled** so good! I hadn't eaten since lunch.

Mom asked, "Are you hungry?" I said, "Yes! How did you know?"

Mom said, "I heard your tummy growl."

14

I didn't know
my tummy made noise.

Dad told my brother, "No burping at the dinner table. Say, **'excuse me'**."

My brother said, "Excuse me."

I didn't hear him burp. It didn't bother me.

We went to a **movie**.

During the movie, my brothers whispered. When I was little, I thought whispers were just moving your mouth. Whispers make noise but they are quieter than indoor voices.

Dad signed and whispered, "Wrappers make noise." We opened them **carefully**.

Sign language doesn't make noise. It doesn't bother anyone.

When Dad drove home, it rained. Hard rain makes a tapping noise.

Lightning flashed a bright light in the sky! I felt a big ka-boom!

23

I said, "What noise does lightning make?"

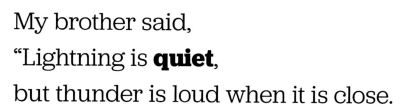

My brother said,
"Lightning is **quiet**,
but thunder is loud when it is close.

Thunderstorms don't bother me.
Do any noises bother you?

26

Rules of Etiquette in Deaf Communities

By Amy Willman, MS in Deaf Education

Etiquette means the standard code of polite behavior in society. Rules of Deaf Etiquette aren't only about making noises or being quiet. Children who grow up deaf or hearing both need to learn polite behaviors in public.

- In general, Deaf people make noise either because they could not hear themselves making the noise, or they have no concept of how noisy it is because of not enough experience.

- Please do not scold Deaf family or friends for making noises. Remember they could not hear it. Instead, ask them to be quieter in a polite way and explain what they did that made too much noise. That way, Deaf people will learn and be more careful next time.

- In general, Deaf people should know where it's okay to make noise and where not to, such as at church, the library, restaurants, or any quiet places.

Rules of Etiquette in Deaf Communities

Do's	Don'ts
Stomp firmly on floor 2 or 3 times	Stomp many times or do this in improper places
Maintain eye contact when talking	Break eye contact (this is considered rude)
Tap lightly on the shoulder 2 times	Tap hard many times or throw objects
Flick lights 2 or 3 times	Flick many times or turn light off
Have a conversation in a bright, well-lighted area	Stand in the front of bright light or window
Pound firmly on a shared surface 2 or 3 times	Pound many times or do this in improper places
Use Sign Language when deaf persons are present	Stare at signers in a rude or nosy way

** Stomping on the floor and pounding on a surface make noises, but they send the vibrations on the floor or surface to get deaf people's attention. Sometimes, deaf people use their voice to describe noises that have no words; such as a car wreck. Deaf people would sign "car smashed another car" and add the voice by trying to sound like a crash noise. Those noises when related to signing are considered normal.

Safe Spaces

Deaf children and adults need to feel safe and comfortable at home and in school or special environments that are part of Deaf Communities. At Deaf Clubs, schools, or social activities, you shouldn't scold or tell children to be quiet when they use their voices related to signing or making more noises than hearing people make in public. Deaf people feel more comfortable by doing noises in their own "safe noise" places. Again remember, they cannot hear the noise. It does not mean they are rude. Deaf people should know the difference when to make noise and when not to make noise. Every day, deaf children—and even adults, too--learn something new that makes noise that they didn't know before.

Deaf Adults' Perspectives

What noise did you learn about when you were older?

ROBERT CHADWICK: Every morning at work, I always dropped my vehicle keys on my desk. I never thought about it at all, it was just my habit. One morning, a guy stopped by my office right after I arrived at work. I asked, "How did you know I just got here?"

My coworker said, "When you drop your keys on your desk, we can hear you."

From then on, I gently set my keys down when I get to work.

RYAN SHEPHARD: I was a beta tester for a company testing wristbands that vibrated when the wristband detected a sound. Depending on the sound's frequency, the wristband vibrated more or less, and I could identify noises like water running or a dog barking.

What I did not know was that it was loud when I peed directly into the water of the toilet bowl. To my great surprise, my vibrating wristband went off like a fire alarm! I decided to shift a bit where it would land against the side of the toilet away from the water. My wristband was suddenly quiet.

I thought, "Over 30 years old, and I know this just now!?" Now, this brings a bigger question: what does this mean all those times I was in public bathrooms before?

GINA GRABHER: When my son was younger, he would tell me, "The car is clicking." I didn't know what was wrong with my car until later I realized the left and right blinkers made noise, too.

"What noises would you teach your deaf child?"

COLLEEN RICHART: Without my daughter's sound support, she is unaware how much louder her voice is when she speaks. She often stood next to her dad working together on something and almost yelled. It hurt her dad's ears! We gave her gentle reminders to lower her voice but never, ever disciplined her for it. She practiced learning quieter self-control. I have also done the same thing and I'm almost 40 years old! Our household will always be loud regardless of our voices. Even our whispering is loud, but that is our norm.

RYAN SHEPHARD: Whatever noise you make, it is safe to assume it's louder than you think, or you might get caught. Many times, I had hoped to be sneakier, but sounds gave me away like eating candy out of a wrapper hidden under the table during dinner.

GINA GRABHER: I remember my mother teaching me how to eat politely. She told me to chew the food more softly because if you open your jaws too much or crunch the food hard with your teeth then people can hear you. I couldn't hear that, so I'm glad my mother told me.

What do Deaf people gain that people who hear don't realize?

COLLEEN RICHART: We rely on vibration and sight more than you assume. We use touch to feel sounds. I can sense vibration differences while I use the lawnmower, weed whacker, or even shoveling dirt and hitting rocks. For example, if the mower is running strangely or something isn't right, we use our hands and body to feel the difference. The same thing goes for driving a car. Also, we can truly enjoy musical concerts without hearing the sound.

GINA GRABHER: We can use sign language when we swim underwater. Also, people have told me that crying babies or children having a tantrum at the store bothers them, but it doesn't bother me.

ROBERT CHADWICK: When I'm taking photographs at hard rock concerts, the bands always play very loud. Hearing patrons have to stand close and shout in each other's ears to communicate. Their jugular veins bulge in their necks while they yell. I can easily sign from far away to my friends who know ASL without the music interfering.

RYAN SHEPHARD: We all know going to Costco is never a great idea when it falls on a Saturday or Sunday Sometimes, we find ourselves there anyway. While the store's bustling with shoppers, I can simply stand on the other side of the aisle more than 50 feet away, putting the product up in the air, signing, "Is this it? No? What did you want?"

Within "eye-shot", we are sparing ourselves from weaving through humans like a game of pinball to ask a family member or friend what products they are looking for. This makes great teamwork and quick in and out of the store!

Bonus videos of Amy Willman demonstrating how to sign the ASL vocabulary words and story, and the Rules of Deaf Etiquette are available on www.kellybrakenhoff.com

The End

About the Contributors

Colleen Richart is the mother of 2 almost-teenagers who are ten-and-a-half months apart in age and has been married to her husband, Stephen, for 14 years. Born in Pennsylvania, Colleen grew up in Omaha. Colleen and her husband are involved in advocating for their children's education and their daughter's deaf education needs. In her free time, Colleen enjoys golfing, spending time with family, and spoiling their two Blue Heeler mixed dogs, Ada and Jayne.

Gina Grabher was born in Lincoln, Nebraska, and grew up mostly in Omaha. Her family moved overseas in high school which sparked her love of traveling all over the USA and world. Gina's son recently graduated from high school and soon her nest will be empty. Her hobbies include camping, walking, hiking, swimming, kayaking or enjoying nature! Gina is a huge animal lover. Her pets include a deaf Red Heeler, 3 kittens, and a Silver Lab puppy.

Ryan Shephard is a Bay Area transplant from Maryland. He gleefully enjoys life on the West coast. He is also a proud dog dad of Koa, a Boxer whom he rescued in early 2019. When Ryan is not working, he spends his time connecting with people from all walks of life and exploring the outdoors. Ryan, as a Deaf native ASL signer, is a strong advocate for accessibility in the Deaf community.

Amy Willman has worked as an American Sign Language Coordinator and Lecturer at the University of Nebraska-Lincoln since 2001. Before moving back to her childhood home in Nebraska, Amy taught elementary school for three years and taught ASL at Santa Fe Community College for six years. Her bachelor's degree in Elementary Level and Studio Arts is from Gallaudet University, the only Deaf university in the world. She earned her master's degree in Deaf Education from McDaniel College. Amy co-authored a book with her mother, Amy Signs: A Mother and Her Deaf Daughter, and their Stories in 2012. Amy did the ASL signs, ASL lesson and videos for Never Mind, the first book in the Duke series. She lives with her four beloved cats, three of whom are deaf.

Robert Chadwick grew up in Auburn, Nebraska, and lived in Omaha and Lincoln before settling down in Columbus, Nebraska. Photographing rock concerts has been Robert's side-profession for the last six years. He also does portrait and family photography. Robert's day job is as a Structural Civil Drafter at Nebraska Public Power District where he has worked for 32 years. His wife Kellie McDermott-Chadwick is originally from Florida, and they have a high-energy four-year-old cat, Keanu. You can see Robert's unique photos and hire him for any special photographic projects by checking out his Facebook page https://www.facebook.com/robertchadwickphotography/. Follow him on Instagram at @rachadw66 or his online concert magazine at @govenue.

Kelly Brakenhoff is an American Sign Language Interpreter whose motivation for learning ASL began in high school when she wanted to converse with her deaf friends. Never Mind, her first children's picture book introducing Duke the Deaf Dog has quickly become popular with children, parents, and educators for promoting inclusive conversations about children with differences. She also writes the Cassandra Sato Mystery series. Kelly is a wife, mom, and grandma, and dog mom to a German Wirehair Pointer.

Theresa Murray has been creating custom art and murals for over 20 years. She pulls from her past as a grooming assistant to inspire the dog personalities for this series. Theresa lives in Omaha, Nebraska with her husband, two sons, and their Westie, Tinkerbell.

Made in the USA
Monee, IL
04 June 2021